مِفْتَاحُ الْقِرَاءةِ وَالْكِتابةِ

BOOK
1

THE KEY TO ARABIC
Fast Track to Reading and Writing Arabic

Dr. Imran Hamza Alawiye

Introduction and Notes for Teachers

'The Key to Arabic' teaches students the skills they need to read and write Arabic. The letters of the alphabet are introduced one at a time, and the student is given the opportunity to read each letter with the various possible combinations of long and short vowels, as well as the 'ay' and 'ow' dipthongs, sukoon and shadda. The use of colour coding in presenting the various vowel sounds helps the student to grasp them more quickly. Each letter is also shown in all its forms: initial, medial, final and isolate so that the student can learn to recognise the letter wherever it appears in the word, as well as how to write it. Clear arrowed diagrams show the student the correct pen direction when writing.

Arabic words are introduced from an early stage, but no word contains letters that the student has not already covered. This assimilative approach enables the student to learn the alphabet in a gradual yet thorough manner, without feeling daunted by the prospect of having to learn the entire alphabet at one go.

Each letter in the first half of the alphabet is covered on a double-page spread. As the student's confidence in reading and writing increases, this is reduced to a single page per letter, and exercises are introduced to reinforce reading and writing skills and to encourage some basic vocabulary acquisition.

For the self-taught student, a quick reference guide to reading skills is provided at the outset to enable him or her to understand the various vowel sounds and gain an overview of the method of joining Arabic letters together to form words, before putting the skill into practice. An optional CD recording of the materials in this workbook is available to help students in mastering correct Arabic pronunciation.

After completing the alphabet, students have the chance to develop their skills further through a set of carefully designed exercises. The first of these (p.55) provides an opportunity for reading and dictation practice, by presenting pairs of similar sounding words. This encourages the student to listen carefully and distinguish between letters that might easily be confused by the non-Arabic-speaker.

Pages 56–59 introduce simple non-verbal sentences using the masculine and feminine forms of "This is...", as well as a wide range of useful vocabulary. Page 60 teaches the alif al-maqsura, with plenty of reading practice. The primary use of 'al' ('the') is taught on pages 61–64, with an explanation of how the following sun and moon letters affect the pronunciation of this word.

Pages 65–68 employ passages of dialogue to teach the student simple useful expressions such as greetings, introducing oneself, asking someone their name and saying goodbye. These dialogues can form the basis for role playing within the classroom setting. The dialogues on page 67 can easily be adapted as a classroom game whereby one student imagines another student to be in one of the places shown on the page, and the rest of the class take turns to ask questions in Arabic to establish the imaginary person's identity and whereabouts.

Having completed "The Key to Arabic" successfully, students should feel comfortable in reading any passage of vocalised text presented to them, and will hopefully have gained the confidence needed to take their study of this challenging language further.

The Arabic Alphabet

Jeem	<u>Th</u>aa	Taa	Baa	Alif
ج	ث	ت	ب	ا
Raa	<u>Dh</u>aal	Daal	<u>Kh</u>aa	Ḥaa
ر	ذ	د	خ	ح
Ḍaad	Ṣaad	<u>Sh</u>een	Seen	Zaa
ض	ص	ش	س	ز
Faa	<u>Gh</u>ayn	ᶜAyn	Ẓa	Ṭa
ف	غ	ع	ظ	ط
Noon	Meem	Laam	Kaaf	Qaaf
ن	م	ل	ك	ق
		Yaa	Waaw	Haa
		ي	و	هـ

3

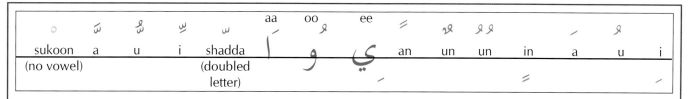

sukoon (no vowel)	a	u	i	shadda (doubled letter)	aa	oo	ee		an	un	un	in	a	u	i

1. The Short Vowels and Tanween

There are three short vowels in Arabic. They are written above or below the Arabic letters.

a) Kasra — This is a short diagonal stroke written below an Arabic letter. It is pronounced 'i', as in the English word 'lip'.

e.g.

Di Ri Wi

If kasra is doubled, it changes the sound from 'i' to 'in' as in the English word 'tin'. This doubling of the vowel is known as "tanween kasra".

e.g.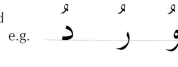

Din Rin Win

b) Damma — This is shaped rather like a small version of the Arabic letter waaw, and it is written above an Arabic letter. It is pronounced 'u', as in the English word 'full'.

e.g.

Du Ru Wu

or — If damma is doubled, it changes the sound from 'u' to 'un' as in the English word 'sun'. This doubling of the vowel is known as "tanween damma". The two dammas are usually written in a joined-up form, though they may also be written separately.

e.g.

Dun Run Wun

c) Fatha
(Say 'fat-ha') — This is a short diagonal stroke written above an Arabic letter. It is pronounced 'a', as in the English word 'dad'.

e.g.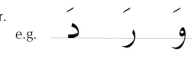

Da Ra Wa

If fatha is doubled, it changes the sound from 'a' to 'an' as in the English word 'man'. It is usually – though not always – supported by an alif. This doubling of the vowel is known as "tanween fatha".

e.g.

Dan Ran Wan

2. Joining up Arabic Letters

Arabic is written from right to left across the page. Arabic words are written in a joined-up form. To achieve this, the letters within a word must be extended to join up with the following letter, unless they are one of the six 'naughty' letters (see overleaf). The letters that are being extended lose their tails in the joining process. The last letter in the word is written in its final form, which usually resembles the isolate or 'by itself' form of the letter, though it is attached to the letter just before it by a short joining line.

You will learn the correct way of joining each letter during the course of this book, but for now, study the following examples to gain an overview of how letters are joined.

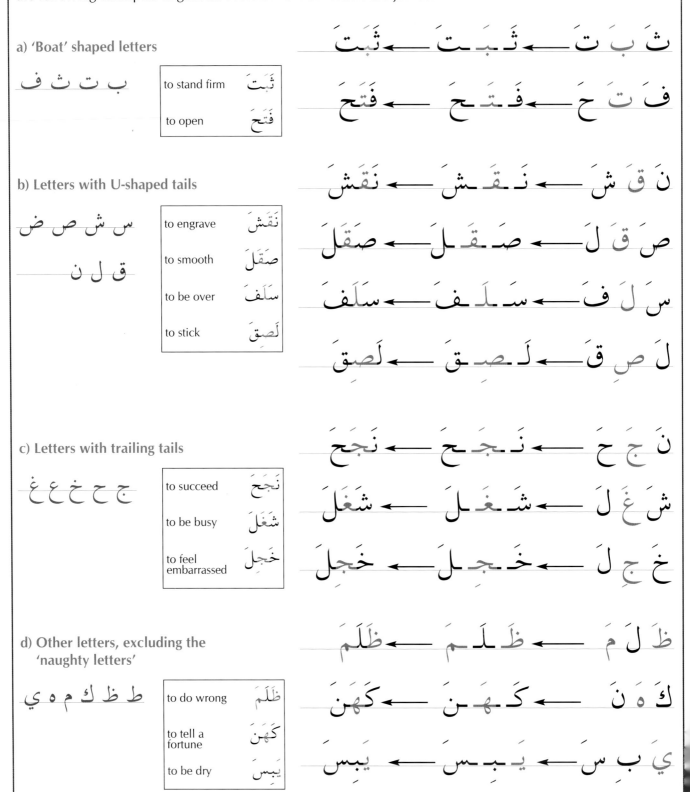

a) 'Boat' shaped letters

ب ت ث ف

to stand firm	ثَبَتَ
to open	فَتَحَ

b) Letters with U-shaped tails

س ش ص ض
ق ل ن

to engrave	نَقَشَ
to smooth	صَقَلَ
to be over	سَلَفَ
to stick	لَصِقَ

c) Letters with trailing tails

ج ح خ غ

to succeed	نَجَحَ
to be busy	شَغَلَ
to feel embarrassed	خَجِلَ

d) Other letters, excluding the 'naughty letters'

ط ظ ك م ه ي

to do wrong	ظَلَمَ
to tell a fortune	كَهَنَ
to be dry	يَبِسَ

sukoon	a	u	i	shadda	aa	oo	ee	an	un	un	in	a	u	i
(no vowel)				(doubled letter)	ا	و	ي							

e) The 'Naughty' Letters

There are six 'naughty' letters, which cannot be extended to the left and as a result should not be connected to the letter in front of them. The six naughty letters are:

و ز ر ذ د ا

ب + ا = با	أ + ب = أب
د + ب = دب	و + ل = لو
ب + د = بد	ل + و = ول

3. The Long Vowels

Three letters of the Arabic alphabet are used to lengthen the sound of the short vowels. These letters are:

و Waaw is used to lengthen the 'u' sound of ḍamma, so it sounds like 'oo' as in 'moon'.

ي Yaa is used to lengthen the 'i' of kasra, so it sounds like 'ee' as in 'knee'.

ا Alif is used to lengthen the 'a' sound of fatḥa, so it sounds like 'aa' ('aardvark').

رُو	جُو	بُو	رِي	جِي	بِي	رَا	جَا	بَا
Roo	Joo	Boo	Ree	Jee	Bee	Raa	Jaa	Baa

When alif itself is lengthened by an alif, it becomes an extra long 'aa' sound called alif al-madd, which is written like this: آ e.g. 'Aaameen' (amen): آمين.

When a laam is followed by an alif, there is a special way of writing it (called a laam-alif) which looks like this: لَا or, when the laam is preceded by another letter, like this: ـلا e.g. سَلَامٌ، لَامِعٌ.

'laami'un' 'salaamun'
(shining) (peace)

4. Sukoon

 A sukoon is a small circle placed on an Arabic letter to indicate the absence of a vowel upon the letter. The letter on which a sukoon is placed must be assimilated to (i.e. slid together with) the sound of the last vowel before it, even if that vowel is at the end of the previous word.

كَمْ	زُرْ	فِرْ	مُرْ	نَمْ	قِف
Kam	Zur	Fir	Mur	Nam	Qif

5. Shadda

Shadda is a symbol written above a letter to show that the letter has been doubled, and therefore sounds stronger. The short vowels are written with a shadda like this:

	or	بِرِّ = رِ + رْ + بِ	رَبَّ = بَ + بْ + رَ	أُمَّ = مَ + مْ + أُ

Hamza: ء and Alif: ا

Hamza, known as a glottal stop in English, is an Arabic consonant that often accompanies tanween, sukoon, or short vowels. Hamza is itself often accompanied by a supporting letter or 'chair' which may take many forms, depending on rather complex rules that we needn't explore here. The various ways in which hamza may appear are shown below. For the purpose of reading, it is best to ignore the 'chair' hamza is sitting on and to concentrate on reading the vowel sound that the hamza is supporting.

Alif, on its own, is a weak letter that takes the sound of any vowel accompanying or preceding it.

| Alif | Hamza |

Copy each row twice onto the lines provided and practise reading the sounds.

إِ ءِ ىِ ئِ ئِ أُ ؤُ ئُ ءُ ئُ ى ؤ أَ ؤَ ئَ ءَ

إِ ئِ ءِ ى ؤ أُ ءُ ئُ ى ؤُ أَ ئَا ؤَا ءَا ءَ

أُ ؤُ ئُ ئُ إِي إِي أُو أُو أَي أَي أَي أَيْ

				aa	oo	ee							
○	ّ	ُّ	ِّ	ّ	ا	و	ي	ً	ٌ	ٍ	ً	ُ	ِ
sukoon	a	u	i	shadda				an	un	un	in	a	u	i
(no vowel)				(doubled letter)									

Copy each row twice onto the lines provided and practise reading the sounds.

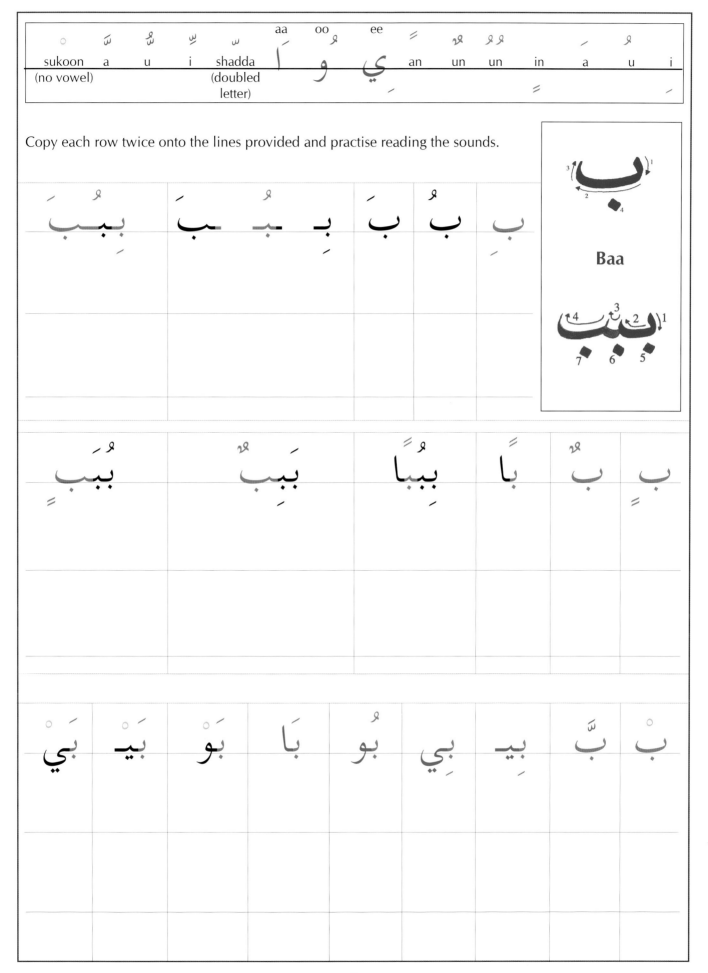

Baa

8

Copy each row onto the lines provided and practise reading the words.

my door	a door	my father	a father
بَابِي بَاب	بَاب	أَبِي	أَب

بَاب

a door

my father

أَبِي

source, core	he said 'daddy'	dad	August
بُؤْبُؤ	بَأْبَأَ	بَابَا	آب

Dad!

بَابَا !

sukoon (no vowel)	a	u	i	shadda (doubled letter)	اوي	aa oo ee	an	un	un	in	a	u	i

Copy each row twice onto the lines provided and practise reading the sounds.

Taa

Taa Marboota (tied up taa)

10

Copy each row onto the lines provided and practise reading the words.

I repent	definitely	a mulberry	she perished
أَتُوبُ	بَتَاتًا	تُوتٌ	تَبَّتْ

repentance	dislike; pride	he stayed overnight	a house
تَوْبَةٌ	إِبَاءَةٌ	بَاتَ	بَيْتٌ

a house

بَيْتٌ

mulberry

تُوتٌ

he repented

تَابَ

sukoon (no vowel)	ﹾ	ﹷ a	ﹹ u	ﹻ i	shadda (doubled letter)	aa ا	oo و	ee ي ﹻ	ﹻ	ﹱ an	ﹹ un	ﹹ un	ﹻ in	ﹷ a	ﹹ u	ﹻ i

Copy each row twice onto the lines provided and practise reading the sounds.

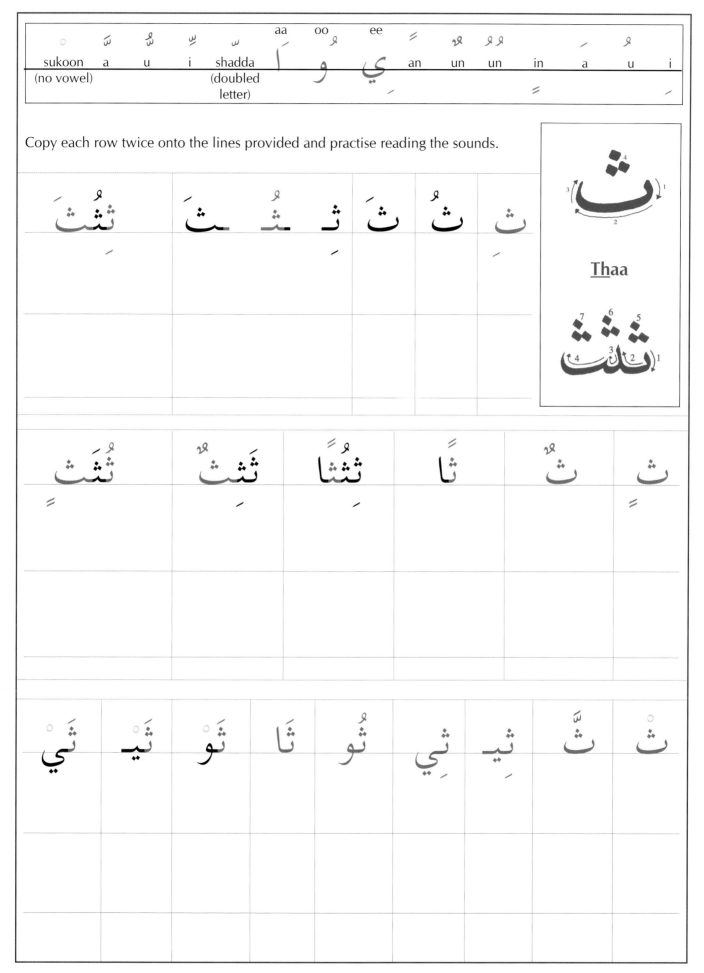

Thaa

12

Copy each row onto the lines provided and practise reading the words.

he withstood	establishment	garment; dress	furniture
ثَبَتَ	إِثْبَاتٌ	ثَوْبٌ	أَثَاثٌ

furniture

أَثَاثٌ

a dress, gown

ثَوْبٌ

stabilization	he yawned	he spread, scattered	abundant growth
تَثْبِيتٌ	تَثَاءَبَ	بَثَّ	أَثِيثٌ

my furniture

أَثَاثِي

sukoon (no vowel)	a	u	i	shadda (doubled letter)	aa ا	oo و	ee ي	ً an	ٌ un	un	in	a	u	i

Copy each row twice onto the lines provided and practise reading the sounds.

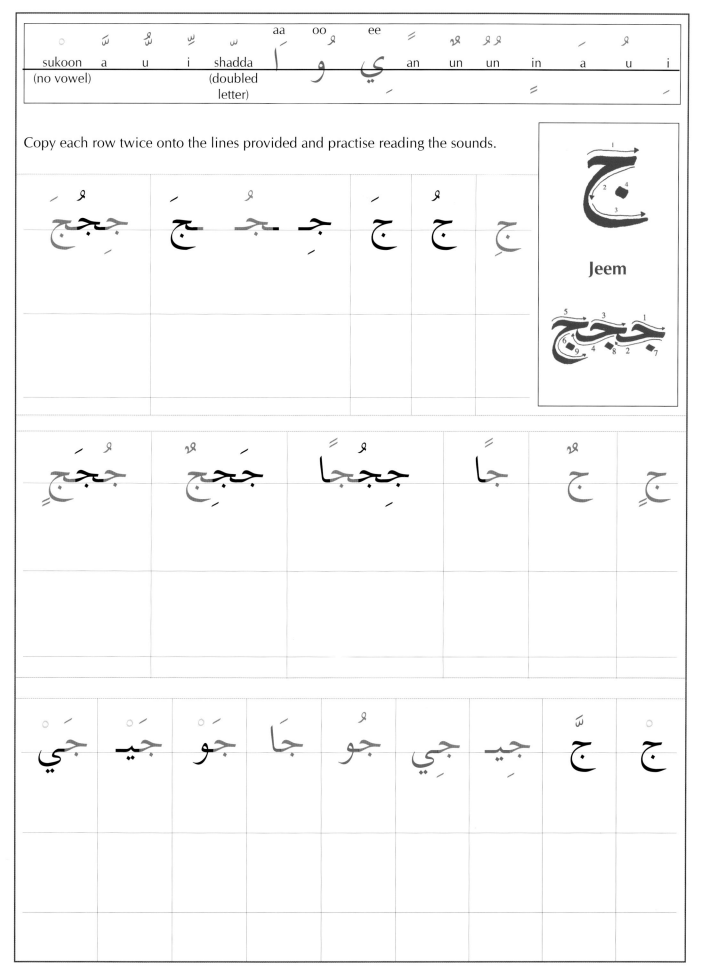

Jeem

14

Copy each row onto the lines provided and practise reading the words.

a coward	a pocket	my pocket	he answered, replied
جَبَأٌ	جَيْب	جَيْبِي	أَجَابَ

a crown

تَاجٌ

a pocket

جَيْب

he came	flowing	a crown	bragging, boasting
جَاءَ	ثَجَّاجًا	تَاجٌ	تَبَجُّج

a coward

جَبَأٌ

sukoon	a	u	i	shadda	aa	oo	ee		an	un	un	in	a	u	i
(no vowel)				(doubled letter)	ا	و	ي								

Copy each row twice onto the lines provided and practise reading the sounds.

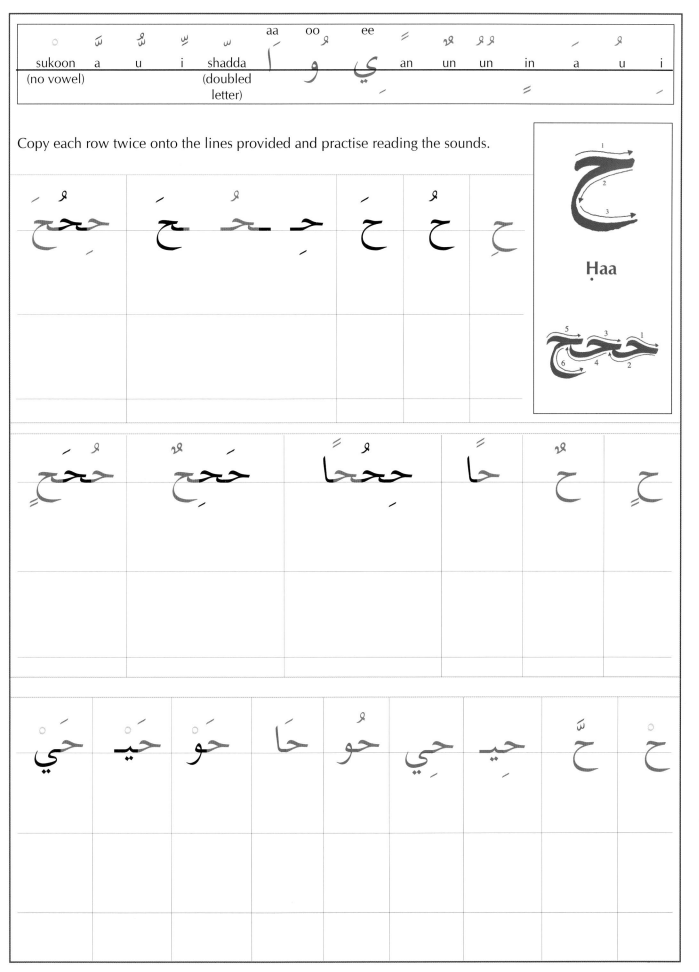

Ḥaa

16

Copy each row onto the lines provided and practise reading the words.

pilgrims	hijab, headscarf	seeds	a watermelon
حُجَّاج	حِجَاب	حُبُوب	حَبْحَب

a whale

حُوت

pilgrims

حُجَّاج

hijab, a headscarf

حِجَاب

a watermelon

حَبْحَب

he looked for; he researched	protest	under	calamity
بَحَثَ	اِحْتِجَاج	تَحْتَ	جَوْح

sukoon	a	u	i	shadda	aa	oo	ee		an	un	un	in	a	u	i
(no vowel)				(doubled letter)	ا	و	ي								

Copy each row twice onto the lines provided and practise reading the sounds.

Khaa

18

Copy each row onto the lines provided and practise reading the words.

my sister	a wicked person	a peach	he hid, concealed
أُخْتِي	خَبِيثٌ	خَوْخٌ	خَبَأَ

a peach

خَوْخٌ

my brother   my sister

أَخِي   أُخْتِي

Excellent! Bravo!	a brother	a nozzle	my brother
بَخْ بَخْ	أَخْ	بَخَّاخَةٌ	أَخِي

a nozzle

بَخَّاخَةٌ

				aa	oo	ee						
◦	ﹷ	ﹹ	ﹻ	ّ	اَ	وُ	يْ		انً	ـٌ	ـٌ	انٍ	ﹷ ﹹ
sukoon	a	u	i	shadda					an	un	un	in	a u
(no vowel)				(doubled letter)									

Copy each row twice onto the lines provided and practise reading the sounds.

Daal

20

Copy each row onto the lines provided and practise reading the words.

a riding animal	a worm	a bear	a chicken
دَابَّةٌ	دُودَةٌ	دُبٌّ	دَجَاجَةٌ

a bear

دُبٌّ

a worm

دُودَةٌ

my grandfather	a grandfather	he began	sound of footsteps
جَدِّي	جَدٌّ	بَدَأَ	دَبْدَبَةٌ

a chicken, hen

دَجَاجَةٌ

21

sukoon (no vowel)	a	u	i	shadda (doubled letter)	aa oo ee ا و ي	an	un	un	in	a	i

Copy each row twice onto the lines provided and practise reading the sounds.

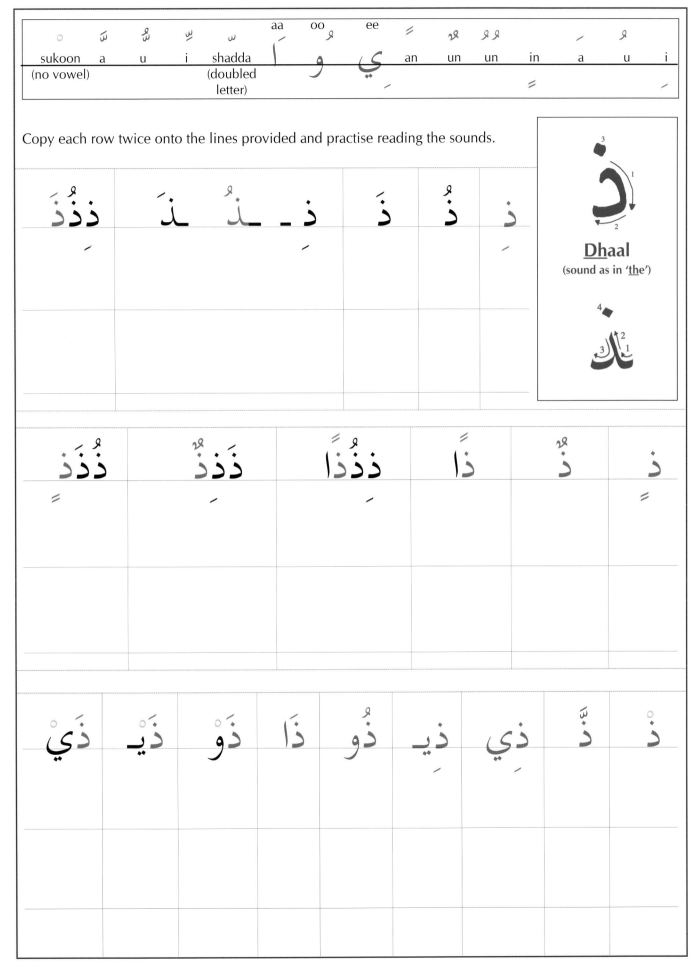

Dhaal
(sound as in 'the')

22

Copy each row onto the lines provided and practise reading the words.

he slaughtered	a lock of hair	a fly	a wolf
ذَبَحَ	ذُؤَابَةٌ	ذُبَابَةٌ	ذِئْبٌ

a shoe

حِذَاءٌ

a wolf

ذِئْبٌ

a shoe	swinging (like a pendulum)	he took	how lovely/excellent!
حِذَاءٌ	تَذَبْذَبَ	أَخَذَ	حَبَّذَا

a fly

ذُبَابَةٌ

Find a word on the right that matches a picture on the left, then write it out in its joined-up form next to the correct picture.

1. ـــ

2. ـــ

3. ـــ

4. ـــ

5. ـــ

6. ـــ

7. ـــ

8. ـــ

9. ـــ

10. ـــ

أَثَاثٌ

بَابٌ

بَيْتٌ

تُوتٌ

تَاجٌ

ثَوْبٌ

جَيْبٌ

حِجَابٌ

حُوتٌ

حَجَّاجٌ

Find a word on the right that matches a picture on the left, then write it out in its joined-up form next to the correct picture.

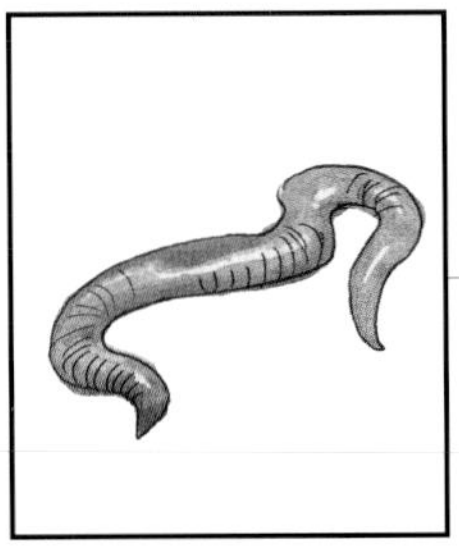

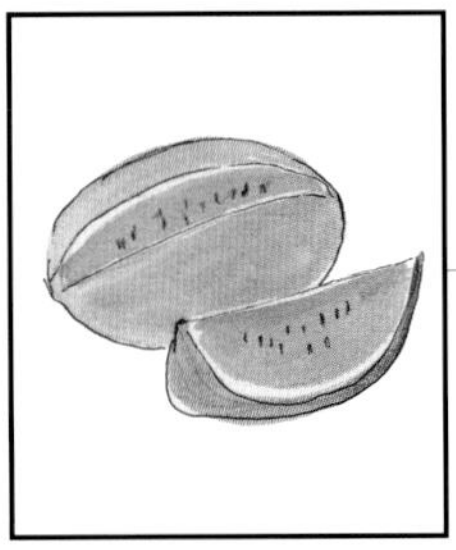

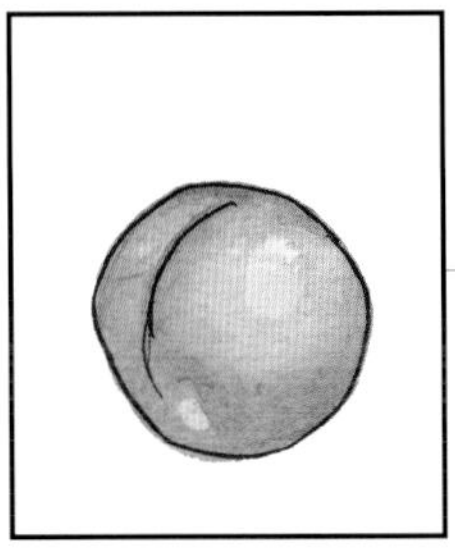

Picture		Word
	11.	أَ بِ ي
	12.	جُ بَّ أُ
	13.	حَ بْ حَ ب
	14.	حِ ذَ ا ء
	15.	خَ وْ خُ
	16.	دُ بّ
	17.	دَ جَ ا جَ ة
	18.	دُ و دَ ة
	19.	ذُ بَ ا بَ ة
	20.	ذِ ئْ بُ

sukoon (no vowel)	a	u	i	shadda (doubled letter)	ٱَ	ي	و		an	un	un	in	a	u	i
○	◌َ	◌ُ	◌ِ	◌ّ	aa	oo ◌ُ	ee	≈	◌ً	◌ٌ	◌ٌ	◌ٍ	◌َ	◌ُ	◌ِ

Copy each row twice onto the lines provided and practise reading the sounds.

Raa

26

Copy each row onto the lines provided and practise reading the words.

a bicycle	corn, maize	Rajab (name of month)	my Lord
دَرَّاجَةٌ	ذُرَةٌ	رَجَبٌ	رَبِّي

a bicycle

دَرَّاجَةٌ

a bull

ثَوْرٌ

a chameleon

حِرْبَاءُ

corn, maize

ذُرَةٌ

test, experiment	a bull	reward; pay, wages	post, mail
إِخْتِبَارٌ	ثَوْرٌ	أَجْرٌ	بَرِيدٌ

27

					aa	oo	ee								
sukoon	a	u	i	shadda	ا	و	ي	an	un	un	in	a	u	i	
(no vowel)				(doubled letter)											

Copy each row twice onto the lines provided and practise reading the sounds.

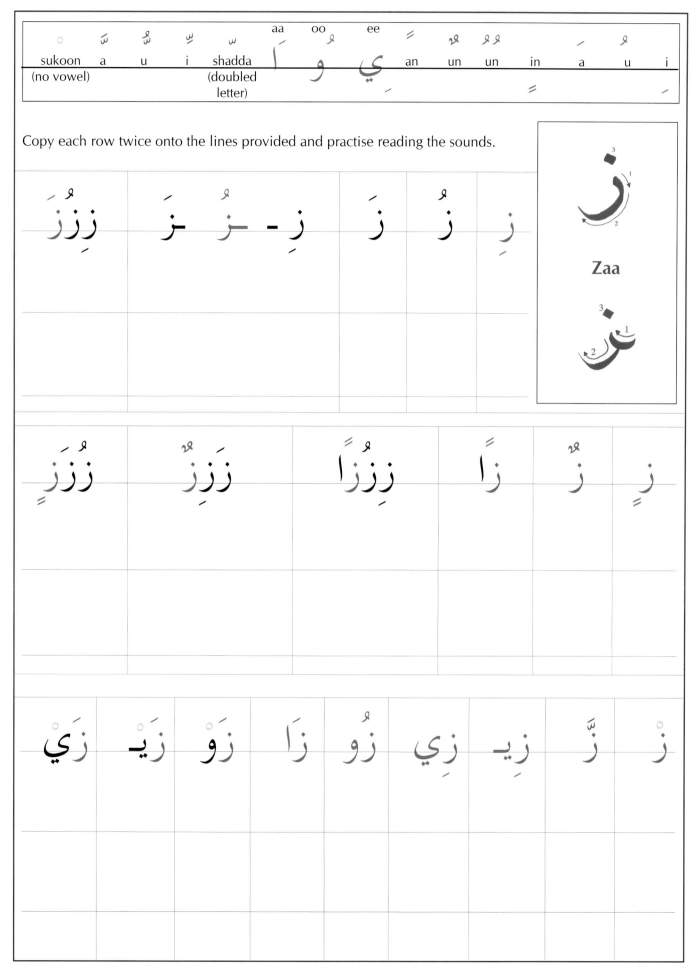

Zaa

28

Copy each row onto the lines provided and practise reading the words.

butter	oil	a drinking glass, tumbler	a lie, falsehood
زُبْدَةٌ	زَيْتٌ	زُجَاجَةٌ	زُورٌ

a butcher

جَزَّارٌ

carrots

جَزَرٌ

carrots	a butcher	a place of safety	bread
جَزَرٌ	جَزَّارٌ	حِرْزٌ	خُبْزٌ

bread

خُبْزٌ

					aa	oo	ee							
sukoon	a	u	i	shadda	ا	و	ي	an	un	un	in	a	u	i
(no vowel)				(doubled letter)										

Copy each row twice onto the lines provided and practise reading the sounds.

Seen

30

Copy each row onto the lines provided and practise reading the words.

a prayer mat	a bed	a computer	a bridge
سَجَّادَةٌ	سَرِيرٌ	حَاسُوبٌ	جِسْرٌ

a prayer mat
سَجَّادَةٌ

a bed
سَرِيرٌ

a computer
حَاسُوبٌ

a sum; an account	glorification of God	teaching	a head
حِسَابٌ	تَسْبِيحٌ	تَدْرِيسٌ	رَأْسٌ

a bridge
جِسْرٌ

31

				aa	oo	ee							
○	َ	ُ	ِ	ّ	ا	و	ي	ً	ٌ	ٍ	ً	ُ	ِ
sukoon	a	u	i	shadda				an	un	un	in	a	i
(no vowel)				(doubled letter)									

Copy each row twice onto the lines provided and practise reading the sounds.

Sheen

32

Copy each row onto the lines provided and practise reading the words.

insects	wood	old age; grey hair	a tree
حَشَرَات	خَشَبٌ	شَيْبٌ	شَجَرَةٌ

a tree

شَجَرَةٌ

insects

حَشَرَاتٌ

a feather

رِيشَةٌ

she is drinking

تَشْرَبُ

bringer of good news	she drinks	a smile	feathers
بَشِيرٌ	تَشْرَبُ	بَشَاشَةٌ	رِيشٌ

Copy each row twice onto the lines provided and practise reading the sounds.

Ṣaad

Copy each row onto the lines provided and practise reading the words.

morning	voice	a picture	a mat
صَبَاحٌ	صَوْتٌ	صُورَةٌ	حَصِيرَةٌ

a pear

إِجَّاصٌ

a rocket

صَارُوخٌ

a person, individual	cheap	pears	particular, specific
شَخْصٌ	رَخِيصٌ	إِجَّاصٌ	خَاصٌّ

a picture

صُورَةٌ

a bus

بَاصٌ

Copy each row twice onto the lines provided and practise reading the sounds.

ض

Ḍaad

Copy each row onto the lines provided and practise reading the words.

civilisation	a molar tooth	light	noise, din
حَضَارَةٌ	ضِرْسٌ	ضَوْءٌ	ضَجِيجٌ

a molar tooth

ضِرْسٌ

earth, ground	eggs	lowest point	green
أَرْضٌ	بَيْضٌ	حَضِيضٌ	أَخْضَرُ

an egg

بَيْضَةٌ

green

أَخْضَرُ

Find a word on the right that matches a picture on the left, then write it out in its joined-up form next to the correct picture.

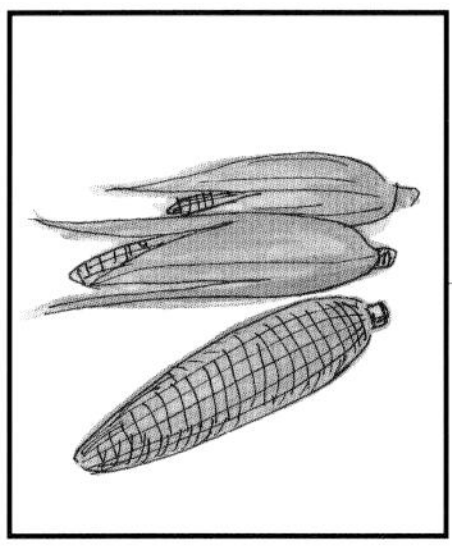

1. _____

2. _____

3. _____

4. _____

5. _____

6. _____

7. _____

8. _____

9. _____

10. _____

ثَ وْ رُ

جَ زَّ ارُ

جَ زَ رُ

حَ ا سُ وْ بُ

حِ رْ بَ اءُ

خُ بْ زُ

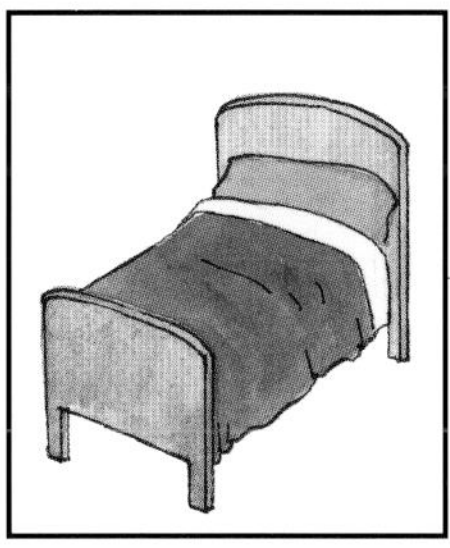

دَ رَّ اجَ ةُ

ذُ رَ ةُ

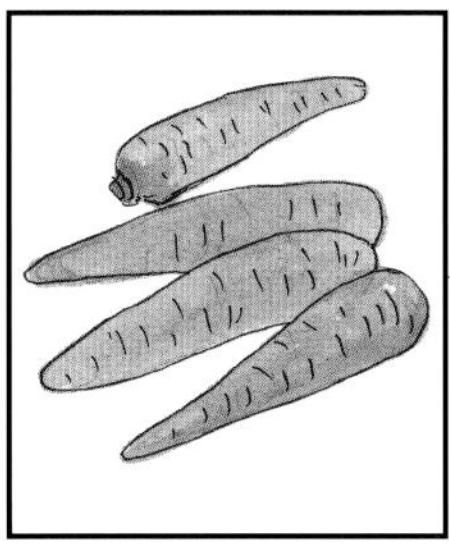

سَ جَّ ا دَ ةُ

سَ رِ يْ رُ

Find the missing letters in the box on the right to complete each word so that it matches its picture.

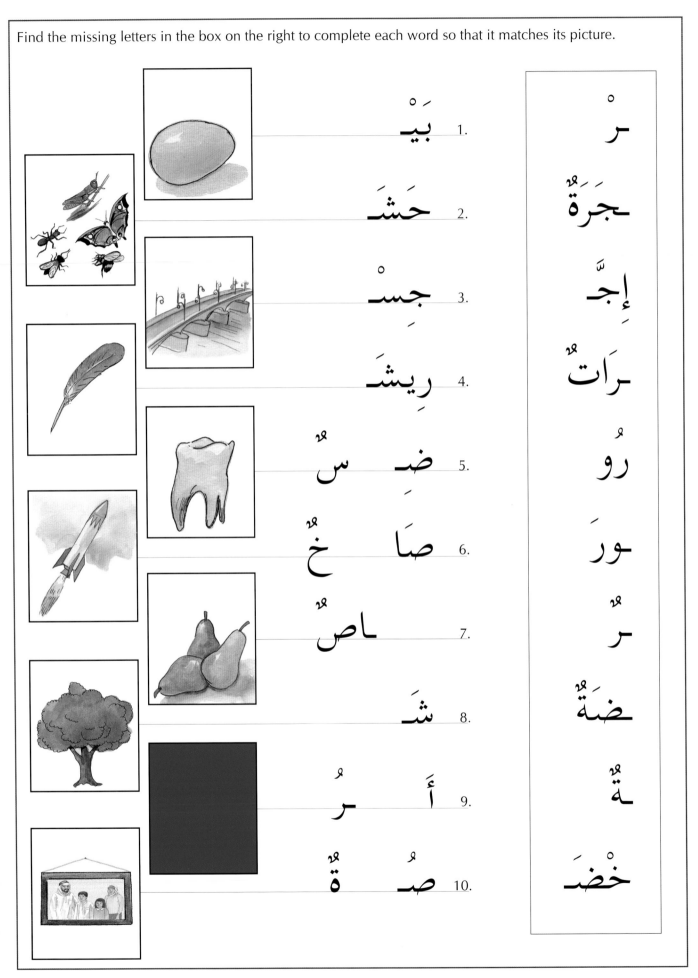

1. بَيْـ‍ـةٌ	ـر ْ
2. حَشَـ‍ـ	جَرَّةٌ
3. جِسْـ‍ـ	إِجَّ
4. رِيشَـ‍ـ	ـرَاتٌ
5. ضِـ‍ـ س ّ	رُو
6. صَا خ ّ	ـورَ
7. ـاصٌ ّ	ـر ّ
8. شَـ‍ـ	ـضَّةٌ
9. أُ‍ـ رُ	ـةٌ
10. صُـ‍ـةٌ	خْضَـ‍

39

					aa	oo	ee					
○	َّ	ُّ	ِّ	ّ	ا	و	ي	ً	ٌ	ٍ	َ	ُ
sukoon	a	u	i	shadda				an	un	un	in	a	u	i
(no vowel)				(doubled letter)								

Copy each row twice onto the lines provided and practise reading the sounds.

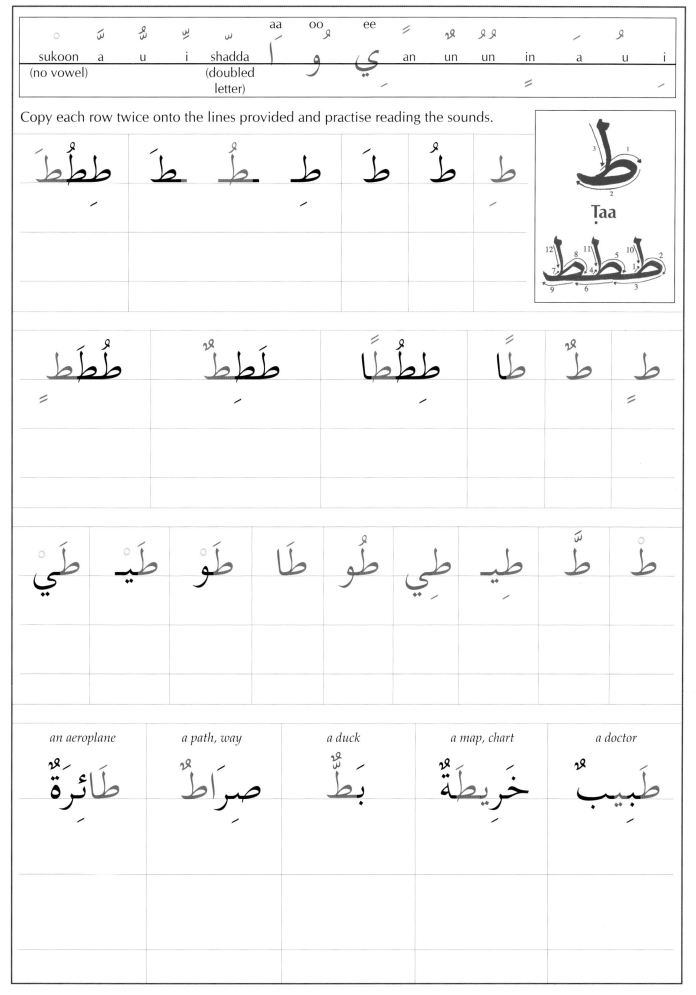

Ṭaa

an aeroplane	a path, way	a duck	a map, chart	a doctor
طَائِرَةٌ	صِرَاطٌ	بَطٌّ	خَرِيطَةَ	طَبِيبٌ

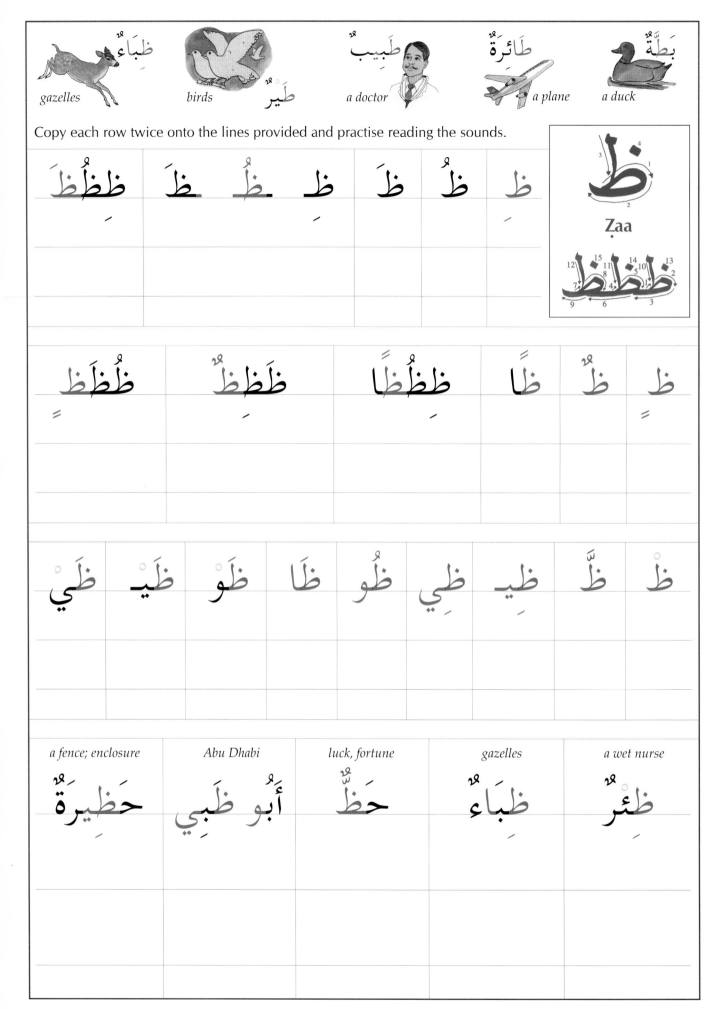

gazelles   birds   a doctor   a plane   a duck

Copy each row twice onto the lines provided and practise reading the sounds.

Zaa

a fence; enclosure	Abu Dhabi	luck, fortune	gazelles	a wet nurse

41

	٥	ّ	ّ	ّ	shadda	aa oo ee		ً ٌ ٌ	ٍ	ً	ُ	ِ
	sukoon	a	u	i	shadda	ا و ي		an un un	in	a	u	i
	(no vowel)				(doubled letter)							

Copy each row twice onto the lines provided and practise reading the sounds.

'Ayn

an arm	a finger	a clock	happy	an old woman
ذِرَاعٌ	إِصْبَعٌ	سَاعَةٌ	سَعِيدٌ	عَجُوزٌ

42

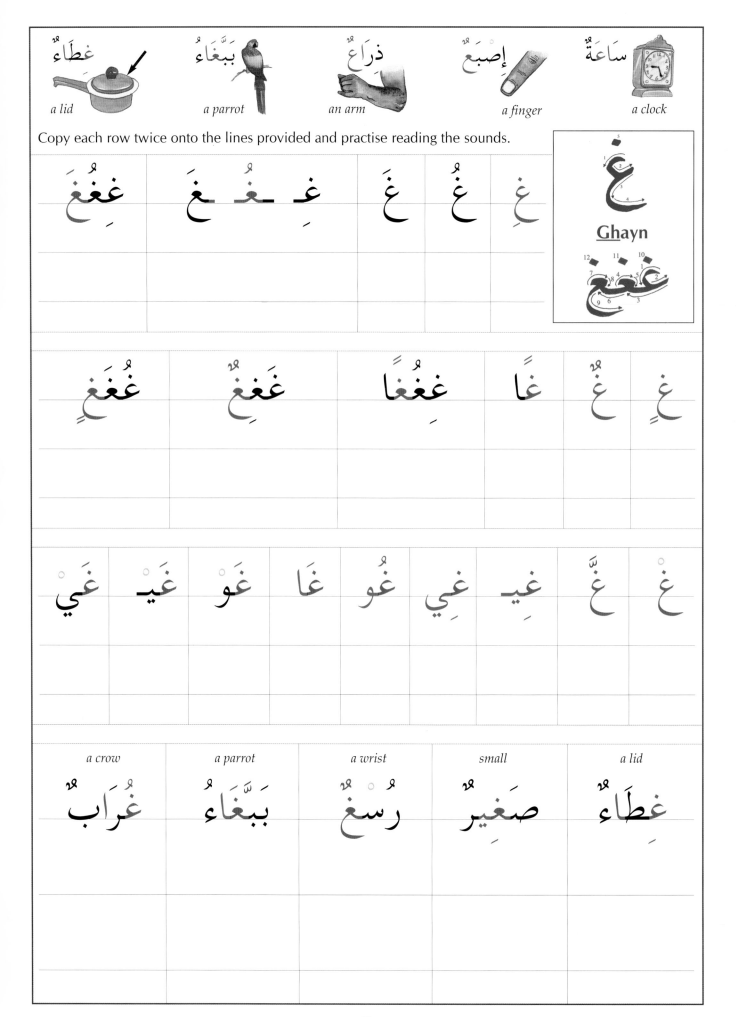

غِطَاء
a lid

بَبَّغَاء
a parrot

ذِرَاع
an arm

إصبَع
a finger

سَاعَة
a clock

Copy each row twice onto the lines provided and practise reading the sounds.

Ghayn
غ

غِغُغِ	غَ ـغـ غِ	غُ	غُ	غِ غُ

غُغُغِ	غُغِ	غِغُغا	غَا	غِ غُ

غَيْ غَيـ غِي	غَو غَا غُو غِي	غَيـ غُ غِ

a crow	*a parrot*	*a wrist*	*small*	*a lid*
غُرَاب	بَبَّغَاء	رُسْغ	صَغِير	غِطَاء

43

Copy each row twice onto the lines provided and practise reading the sounds.

Faa

an envelope	a pavement, sidewalk	a room	a whistle	a butterfly
ظَرْف	رَصيف	غُرْفَة	صَفّارَة	فَرَاشَة

44

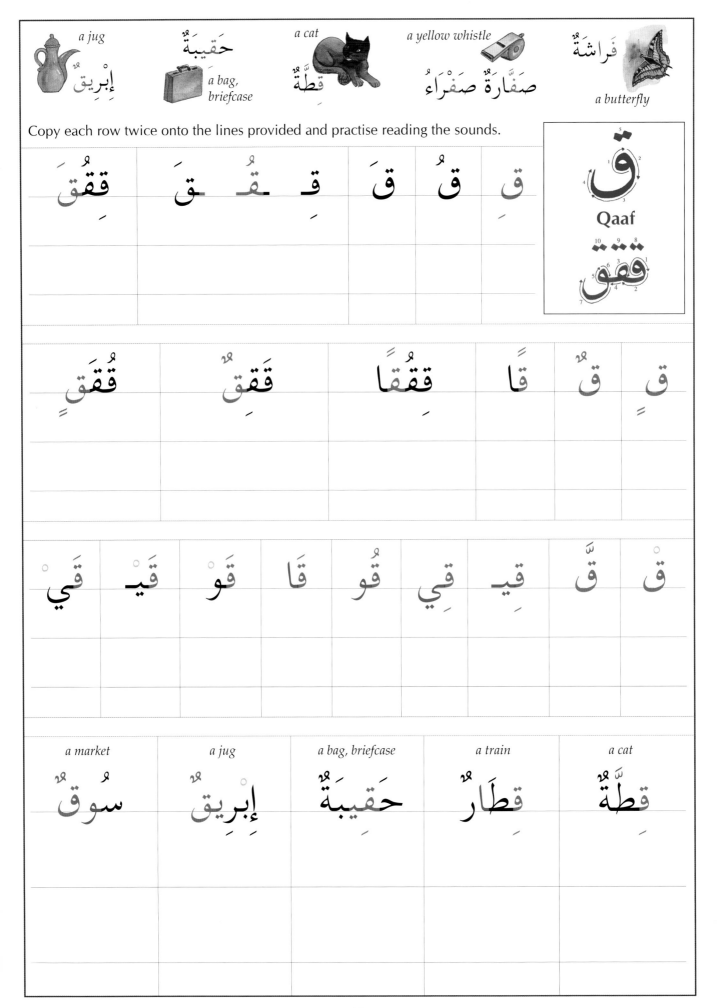

Copy each row twice onto the lines provided and practise reading the sounds.

a jug — إِبْرِيقُ

a bag, briefcase — حَقِيبَةٌ

a cat — قِطَّةٌ

a yellow whistle — صَفَّارَةٌ صَفْرَاءُ

a butterfly — فَرَاشَةٌ

ق
Qaaf
قمق

قُقَ | قَ قُ قِ | قَ قُ | قُ قَ | ق

قُقَ | قَقِ | قَقُقَا | قَ قَا | قُ ق

قَيْ | قَيْ قِ | قُو قَا | قَي قِي | قَ ق

a market	a jug	a bag, briefcase	a train	a cat
سُوقٌ	إِبْرِيقٌ	حَقِيبَةٌ	قِطَارٌ	قِطَّةٌ

45

Break up each word on the right into its separate letters, then rewrite it in its joined form. Write the meaning of the word in English in the left hand column. The first one has been done for you.

a doctor	طَبِيبٌ	طَ ب ي ب	طَبِيبٌ e.g.
			طَائِرَةٌ 1.
			تَسْبِيحٌ 2.
			رَخِيصٌ 3.
			ظِبَاءٌ 4.
			سَاعَةٌ 5.
			إِصْبَعٌ 6.
			ذِرَاعٌ 7.
			بَبَّغَاءُ 8.
			غِطَاءٌ 9.
			فَرَاشَةٌ 10.

46

Break up each word on the right into its separate letters, then rewrite it in its joined form. Write the meaning of the word in English in the left hand column. The first one has been done for you.

a room	غُرْفَةٌ	عُ رْ فَ ةٌ	غُرْفَةٌ e.g.
			إِبْرِيقٌ 11.
			صَفَّارَةٌ 12.
			قِطَّةٌ 13.
			حَقِيبَةٌ 14.
			رُسْغٌ 15.
			قِطَارٌ 16.
			ضَجِيجٌ 17.
			غُرَابٌ 18.
			حَضَارَةٌ 19.
			تَدْرِيسٌ 20.

47

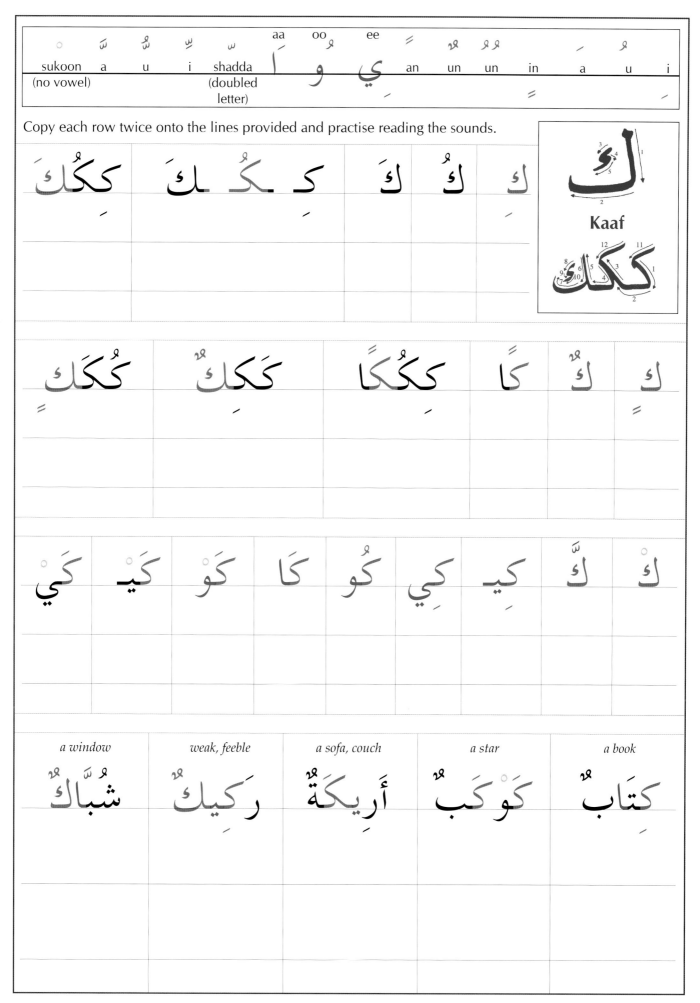

○	ّ	ُّ	ِّ	ّ	aa أ	oo و	ee ي	ً an	ٌ un	ٌ un	ٍ in	َ a	ُ u	ِ i
sukoon	a	u	i	shadda				an	un	un	in	a	u	i
(no vowel)				(doubled letter)										

Copy each row twice onto the lines provided and practise reading the sounds.

Kaaf

a window	weak, feeble	a sofa, couch	a star	a book
شُبَّاك	رَكِيك	أَرِيكَة	كَوكَب	كِتَاب

48

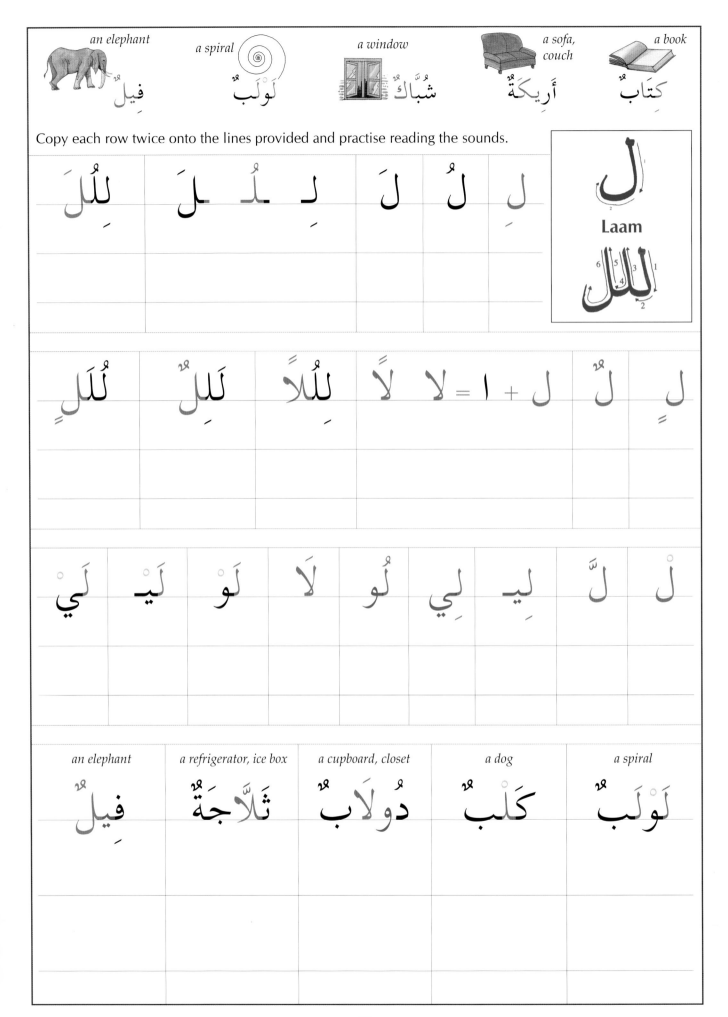

an elephant	a spiral	a window	a sofa, couch	a book
فِيل	لَوْلَب	شُبَّاك	أَرِيكَة	كِتَاب

Copy each row twice onto the lines provided and practise reading the sounds.

ل
Laam
للل

لُلُ لَ لَ لُ لَ لِ لُ لَ لِ لُ لَ ل ل

لُلُل لَلِ لُلُا لَا لَا = ا + ل لُ لُ لِ

لَي لَيْ لَو لَا لُو لِي لِ لَي لَ لُ

an elephant	a refrigerator, ice box	a cupboard, closet	a dog	a spiral
فِيل	ثَلَّاجَة	دُولَاب	كَلْب	لَوْلَب

49

					aa	oo	ee					
sukoon	a	u	i	shadda	ا	و	ي	an	un	un	in	a	u	i
(no vowel)				(doubled letter)									

Copy each row twice onto the lines provided and practise reading the sounds.

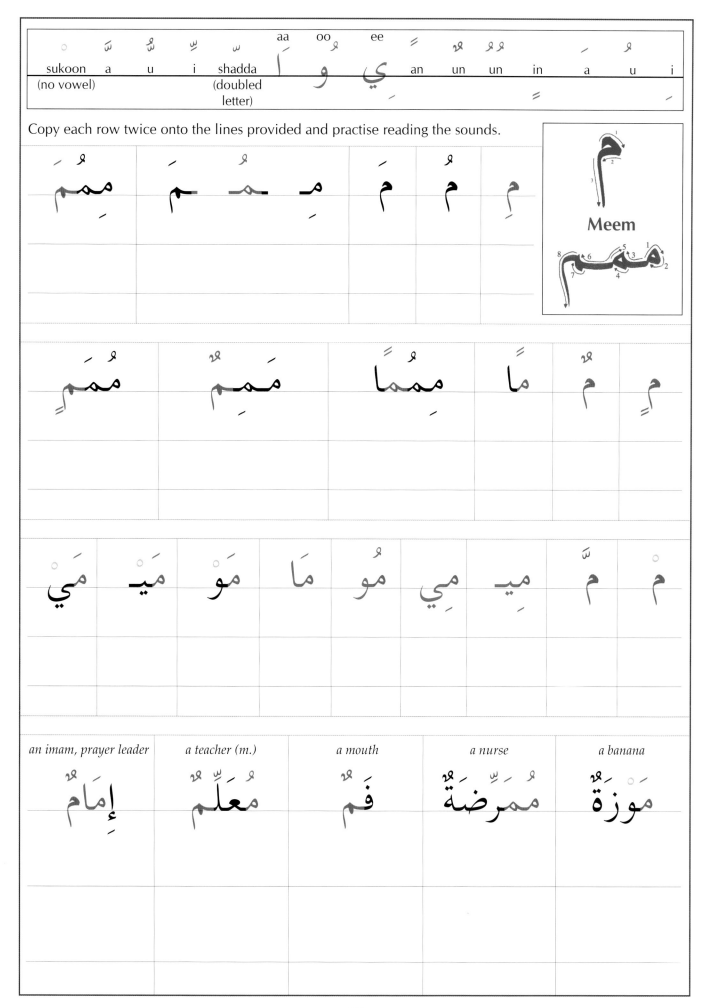

Meem

a banana	a nurse	a mouth	a teacher (m.)	an imam, prayer leader
مَوْزَةٌ	مُمَرِّضَةٌ	فَمٌ	مُعَلِّمٌ	إِمَامٌ

50

an eye	an ostrich	a mouth	a camel	a banana
عَيْن	نَعَامَةٌ	فَمٌ	جَمَلٌ	مَوْزَةٌ

Copy each row twice onto the lines provided and practise reading the sounds.

ن
Noon

ننن

a snake	an eye	a pipe	a box	an ostrich
ثُعْبَانٌ	عَيْن	أُنْبُوبٌ	صُنْدُوقٌ	نَعَامَةٌ

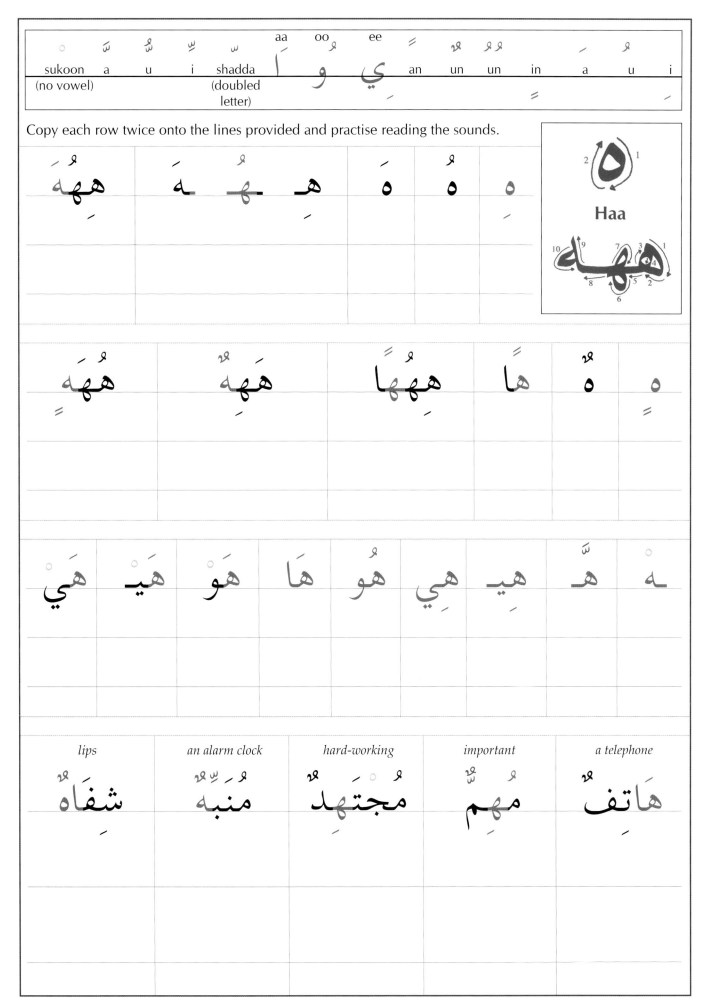

sukoon (no vowel)	a	u	i	shadda (doubled letter)	aa oo ee ا و ي	an	un	un	in	a	u	i

Copy each row twice onto the lines provided and practise reading the sounds.

Haa

lips	an alarm clock	hard-working	important	a telephone
شِفاه	منبه	مجتهد	مهم	هاتِف

52

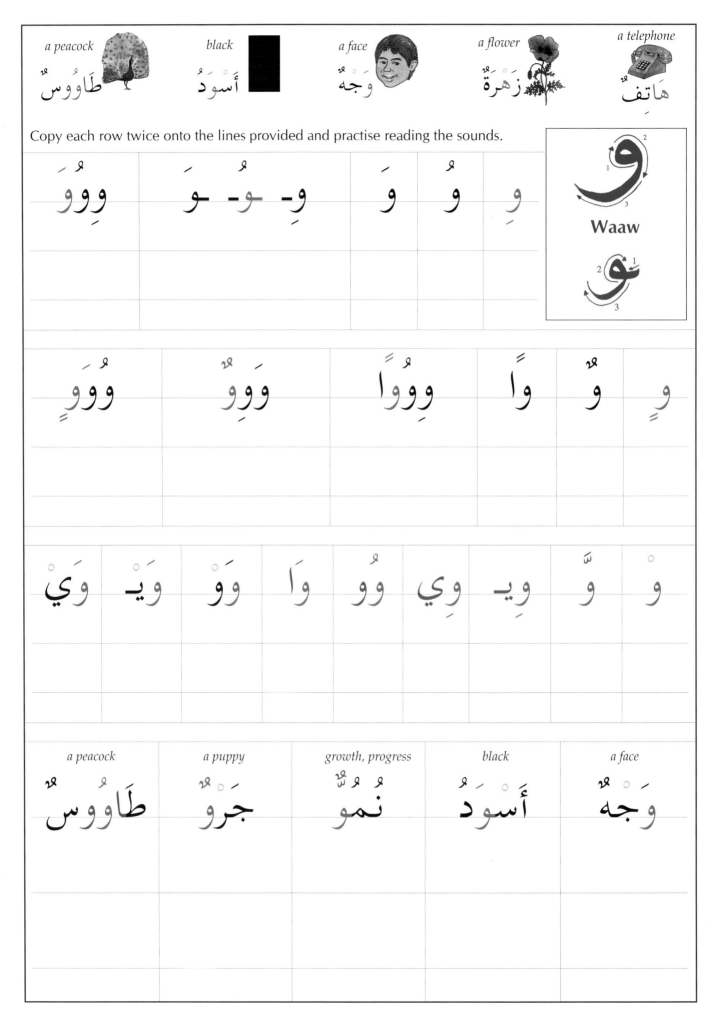

a peacock	black	a face	a flower	a telephone
طَاوُوسٌ	أَسْوَدُ	وَجْهٌ	زَهْرَةٌ	هَاتِفٌ

Copy each row twice onto the lines provided and practise reading the sounds.

Waaw

a peacock	a puppy	growth, progress	black	a face
طَاوُوسٌ	جَرْوٌ	نمو	أَسْوَدُ	وَجْهٌ

53

sukoon (no vowel)	a	u	i	shadda (doubled letter)	aa	oo	ee	an	un	un	in	a	u	i
					ا	و	ي							

Copy each row twice onto the lines provided and practise reading the sounds.

Yaa

grey (gray)	a chair	a kettle	a car	a day
رَمَادِي	كُرْسِي	غَلَايَة	سَيَّارَة	يَوْم

54

Similar Sounding Words

The pairs of words listed below demonstrate the importance of correct pronunciation in Arabic, because the slightest difference in sound can totally change the meaning of a word. Each pair of words below contains similar sounding letters. Practise reading them several times with your Arabic teacher until you can tell them apart. Then ask your teacher to dictate them to you until you can write them down correctly.

English	Arabic	English	Arabic	English	Arabic	English	Arabic
spacious	فَسِيح	eloquent	فَصِيح	clay, soil	طِين	a fig	تِين
check-up; test	فَحْص	awe; respect; prestige	فَأْس	a pilot	طَيَّار	a trend	تَيَّار
desire	حِرْص	inheritance	إِرْث	cleverness	فِطْنَة	discord, civil strife	فِتْنَة
correct	صَوَاب	rewards	ثَوَاب	he measured	كَالَ	he said	قَالَ
direction	صَوْب	dress	ثَوْب	a dog	كَلْب	a heart	قَلْب
glossy	صَقِيل	heavy	ثَقِيل	he deceived	كَادَ	he wrecked	قَاضَ
a pyramid	هَرَم	holy; forbidden	حَرَم	after	بَعْد	some	بَعْض
he strove, endeavoured	جَهَد	he denied	جَحَد	a path, trail	دَرْب	beating, hitting	ضَرْب
a river	نَهْر	an axe	نَحْر	a stench, stink	ذَفَر	victory, triumph	ظَفَر
a worker (m)	عَامِل	pregnant	حَامِل	he vowed	نَذَر	he looked	نَظَر
confession, admission	اِعْتِرَاف	profession, trade	اِحْتِرَاف	flowers	زُهُور	appearance	ظُهُور
a brain	عَقْل	food	أَكْل	he whistled	صَفَر	he travelled	سَفَر
strangeness	غَرَابَة	ruin	خَرَابَة	he poured	صَبّ	he insulted	سَبّ
excess	غُلُوّ	emptiness	خُلُوّ	son-in-law	صِهْر	sorcery	سِحْر

This is ...

If you want to say 'This is a (something)' in Arabic, you need to know whether the thing you are introducing is masculine or feminine. Many singular feminine nouns in Arabic end in a 'tied taa' (taa marbuta) and are therefore easily recognisable. Most singular nouns that do not end in taa marbuta are masculine.

In Arabic, the verb 'to be' is not usually used in the present tense, so you don't need a separate word for 'is' in the sentences that follow, because the idea of 'is' is implied in the word for 'this'.

The masculine word for 'This is' in Arabic is: هَذَا which is pronounced 'haadha', as if it has a long 'aa' sound after the haa. For example: This is a (male) teacher: هَذَا مُعَلِّمٌ. (haadha mu'allimun)

The feminine word for 'This is' in Arabic is: هَذه which is pronounced 'haadhihi', again, as if it has a long 'aa' sound after the haa at the beginning of the word.

For example: This is a (female) teacher: هَذه مُعَلِّمَةٌ. (haadhihi mu'allimatun)

Practise reading the following sentences and learn the words and their meanings.
Copy each sentence out onto the line provided.

| *This is a chair.* | *This is a lock.* | *This is a drum.* | *This is a (pair of) glasses.* | *This is a book.* |
| هَذَا كُرْسِيٌّ. | هَذَا قُفْلٌ. | هَذَا طَبْلٌ. | هَذه نَظَّارَةٌ. | هَذَا كِتَابٌ. |

| *This is a knife.* | *This is a fork.* | *This is a cup.* | *This is a ball.* | *This is a desk.* |
| هَذَا سِكِّينٌ. | هَذه شَوْكَةٌ. | هَذَا كَأْسٌ. | هَذه كُرَةٌ. | هَذه منْضَدَةٌ. |

56

Write a sentence in Arabic under each picture using the correct form of "This is", following the examples on the opposite page. The words ending in taa marbuta are all feminine: the rest are masculine.

This is a table.	This is a cherry.	This is an apricot	This is a lemon.	This is a fridge (ice box).

طَاوِلَةٌ	كَرَزٌ	مِشْمِشٌ	لَيْمُونٌ	ثَلَّاجَةٌ

This is a rabbit.	This is a squirrel.	This is a prayer mat.	This is a candle.	This is a (piece of) meat.
			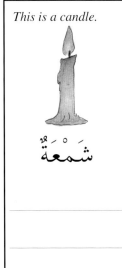	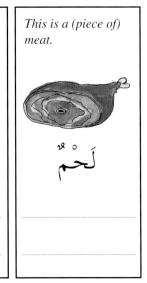
أَرْنَبٌ	سِنْجَابٌ	سَجَّادَةٌ	شَمْعَةٌ	لَحْمٌ

This is a fish.	This is a pig.	This is a horse.	This is a snake.	This is a lion.

سَمَكَةٌ	خِنْزِيرٌ	حِصَانٌ	ثُعْبَانٌ	لَبْوَةٌ

Using the vocabulary you have learned during the course of this book to help you, label the arrowed items in the following pictures, beginning each label with the correct form of 'This is'. Two items have been done for you by way of example.

هَذَا كُرْسِيٌّ.
This is a chair.

This is a fork.

This is a candle.

هَذِه طَاوِلَةٌ.
This is a table.

This is a fish.

This is a cup.

This is a ball.

This is a bear.

This is a bicycle.

This is a horse.

This is a pear.

This is a bull.

This is a pig.

This is a bear.

This is a wolf.

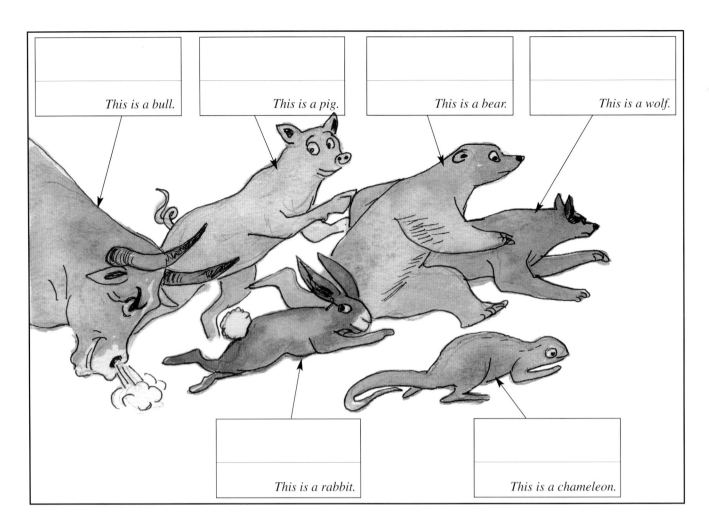

This is a rabbit.

This is a chameleon.

This is a computer.

This is a chicken.

This is a molar.

This is an egg.

This is a lioness.

This is a fridge (icebox).

This is meat.

This is a lock.

Al-Alif al-Maqsura

Some Arabic words have a special kind of alif at the end of them, known as an alif al-maqsura. It has the shape of the letter 'yaa', but without any dots underneath it. It always has a fatha before it, and it is usually pronounced 'aa'. Below are some examples of words ending in al-alif al-maqsura. Practise reading these words, and then copy them out in your exercise book.

hospital	مُسْتَشْفَى	he strove, endeavoured	سَعَى	he built	بَنَى
café	مَقْهَى	he intended	نَوَى	he ran	جَرَى
building	مَبْنَى	he came, arrived	أَتَى	he told, related, reported	حَكَى
lord, master	مَوْلَى	he gave	أَعْطَى	he saw	رَأَى
goal; range	مَرْمَى	it was enough, sufficient	كَفَى	he bought, purchased	اِشْتَرَى
shelter, place of refuge	مَأْوَى	smaller, younger (feminine)	صُغْرَى	he rebelled	عَصَى
Mustafa	مُصْطَفَى	larger, older (feminine)	كُبْرَى	he spent time	قَضَى
Musa (Moses)	مُوسَى	farther, more distant; maximum	أَقْصَى	he forbade, banned	نَهَى
'Isa (Jesus)	عِيسَى	nearer; lower; minimum	أَدْنَى	he walked	مَشَى
Yahya (John)	يَحْيَى	higher	أَعْلَى	he fulfilled (a promise)	وَفَى
Salma	سَلْمَى	higher, superior	أَرْقَى	he cried	بَكَى
Salwa	سَلْوَى	stronger	أَقْوَى	he gave someone a drink	سَقَى
Layla	لَيْلَى	a patient	مَرْضَى	he told, related	رَوَى
Yusra	يُسْرَى	pasture, grazing	مَرْعَى	he refused	أَبَى

The Sun and Moon Letters

So far, the words you have been reading in this book have been indefinite (e.g. **a** book, **an** eye etc., rather than **the** book, **the** eye). Tanween is used on the last letter of a word to show that the word is indefinite. e.g. kitaab**un** – **a** book.

One of the ways of making an Arabic word definite is to attach the word 'al' (meaning 'the') before it. The alif in 'al' is a weak alif, meaning that it can only be pronounced if it is at the beginning of a sentence, (that is to say, when no other letter comes before it). When a word is defined, it can no longer take tanween. Instead, the last letter of the word takes a single vowel (i.e. a fatha, kasra or damma).
e.g. al-kitaab**u** – **the** book.

اَلْ

'the'

The Arabic alphabet, as you may already have realised, has twenty-eight letters. These letters are divided into two equal groups. One group is known as the 'moon letters', and the other as the 'sun letters'.

When the laam in 'al' is followed by one of the moon letters, it automatically takes a sukoon and is pronounced. However, when the laam of 'al' is followed by one of the sun letters, it becomes silent (in other words, it isn't pronounced). When a sun letter comes immediately after the 'al', a shadda must be written on the sun letter.

Study the examples below, and practise reading them aloud:

The Fourteen Moon Letters

ي	و	هـ	م	ك	ق	ف	غ	ع	خ	ح	ج	ب	ا

the mouth	اَلْفَمُ	a mouth	فَمٌ	the sofa	اَلْأَرِيكَةُ	a sofa	أَرِيكَةٌ
the train	اَلْقِطَارُ	a train	قِطَارٌ	the door	اَلْبَابُ	a door	بَابٌ
the chair	اَلْكُرْسِيُّ	a chair	كُرْسِيٌّ	the carrot	اَلْجَزَرُ	a carrot	جَزَرٌ
the teacher	اَلْمُعَلِّمُ	a teacher	مُعَلِّمٌ	the shoe	اَلْحِذَاءُ	a shoe	حِذَاءٌ
the telephone	اَلْهَاتِفُ	a telephone	هَاتِفٌ	the bread	اَلْخُبْزُ	bread	خُبْزٌ
the boy	اَلْوَلَدُ	a boy	وَلَدٌ	the old man	اَلْعَجُوزُ	an old man	عَجُوزٌ
the hand	اَلْيَدُ	a hand	يَدٌ	the room	اَلْغُرْفَةُ	a room	غُرْفَةٌ

Moon letter reading practice

When 'al' (the) is preceded by a word ending in a vowel, the alif becomes silent and the preceding vowel sound is 'slid' together with the laam of the 'al', so it sounds as if there is no space or pause between the words. Therefore, in the first example below, the sentence would read as follows: "Laa tajlis **'alal**-ard." The 'a' sound of the alif al-maqsura is shortened, so that it sounds like a fatḥa. Similarly, in sentence 14 below, the 'ee' sound of 'fee' is shortened as it is slid together with the following word, thus: "Laa taḍa**'il**-yada **fil**-jaybi". It is therefore necessary to look ahead when reading Arabic to see if the sound at the end of one word needs to be slid together with the next word.

Practise reading the sentences below out loud, paying close attention to sliding the sounds together where necessary.

1. Don't sit on the ground.	لَا تَجْلِسْ عَلَى الْأَرْضِ .
2. Ducks like [the] water.	يُحِبُّ الْبَطُّ الْمَاءَ .
3. I like [the] carrots.	أُحِبُّ الْجَزَرَ .
4. This [the] shoe is new.	هَذَا الْحِذَاءُ جَدِيدٌ .
5. This [the] bread is delicious.	هَذَا الْخُبْزُ لَذِيذٌ .
6. I like helping the old man.	أُحِبُّ مُسَاعَدَةَ الْعَجُوزِ .
7. This [the] room is wide.	هَذِهِ الْغُرْفَةُ وَاسِعَةٌ .
8. Don't put the pen in the mouth.	لَا تَضَعِ الْقَلَمَ فِي الْفَمِ .
9. This [the] train is fast.	هَذَا الْقِطَارُ سَرِيعٌ .
10. This [the] chair is broken.	هَذَا الْكُرْسِيُّ مَكْسُورٌ .
11. This [the] teacher is excellent.	هَذَا الْمُعَلِّمُ مُمْتَازٌ .
12. This [the] telephone is modern.	هَذَا الْهَاتِفُ مُعَطَّلٌ .
13. This [the] boy is polite.	هَذَا الْوَلَدُ مُؤَدَّبٌ .
14. Don't put the hand in the pocket.	لَا تَضَعِ الْيَدَ فِي الْجَيْبِ .

The Fourteen Sun Letters

When the laam in 'al' is followed by one of the sun letters, it becomes silent (not pronounced), and a shadda is written on the sun letter, making the sound of the sun letter more intense. So, for example, 'taajun' (a crown), becomes '**att**aaju' (the crown).

Study the examples below, and practise reading them aloud:

ت ث د ذ ر ز س ش ص ض ط ظ ن ل

the tree	اَلشَّجَرَةُ	a tree	شَجَرَةٌ	the crown	اَلتَّاجُ	a crown	تَاجٌ
the whistle	اَلصَّفَّارَةُ	a whistle	صَفَّارَةٌ	the refrigerator	اَلثَّلَاجَةُ	a refrigerator	ثَلَاجَةٌ
the molar tooth	اَلضِّرْسُ	a molar tooth	ضِرْسٌ	the bear	اَلدُّبُّ	a bear	دُبٌّ
the doctor (f.)	اَلطَّبِيبَةُ	a doctor (f.)	طَبِيبَةٌ	the wolf	اَلذِّئْبُ	a wolf	ذِئْبٌ
the envelope	اَلظَّرْفُ	an envelope	ظَرْفٌ	the wrist	اَلرُّسْغُ	a wrist	رُسْغٌ
the ostrich	اَلنَّعَامَةُ	an ostrich	نَعَامَةٌ	the flower	اَلزَّهْرَةُ	a flower	زَهْرَةٌ
the painting	اَللَّوْحَةُ	a painting	لَوْحَةٌ	the bed	اَلسَّرِيرُ	a bed	سَرِيرٌ

As with the moon letter sentences, the last vowel sound on any word before a word beginning with 'al' is 'slid' together with the sun letter. So the first sentence below would read: "Yalbasul-malik**ut-t**aaj**adh-dh**ahabiyya." Practise reading the following sentences out loud.

1. The king is wearing the golden crown.

يَلْبَسُ الْمَلِكُ التَّاجَ الذَّهَبِيَّ .

2. I put the ice in the refrigerator.

وَضَعْتُ الثَّلْجَ فِي الثَّلَاجَةِ .

3. I like the black bear.

أُحِبُّ الدُّبَّ الْأَسْوَدَ .

4. The wolf ate the rabbit.

أَكَلَ الذِّئْبُ الْأَرْنَبَ .

5. This [the] wrist is broken.

هَذَا الرُّسْغُ مَكْسُورٌ .

6. This [the] flower is beautiful.

هَذِهِ الزَّهْرَةُ جَمِيلَةٌ .

7. This [the] bed is comfortable.

هَذَا السَّرِيرُ مُرِيحٌ .

63

8. This [the] tree is old.	هَذِهِ الشَّجَرَةُ قَدِيمَةٌ .
9. The yellow whistle is blocked.	اَلصَّفَارَةُ الصَّفْرَاءُ مَسْدُودَةٌ .
10. This [the] molar tooth is rotten.	هَذَا الضِّرْسُ مُسَوَّسٌ .
11. That [the] doctor (f.) is skilful.	تِلْكَ الطَّبِيبَةُ مَاهِرَةٌ .
12. This [the] envelope is open.	هَذَا الظَّرْفُ مَفْتُوحٌ .
13. The ostrich is faster than the human.	اَلنَّعَامَةُ أَسْرَعُ مِنَ الْإِنْسَانِ .
14. This [the] painting is beautiful.	هَذِهِ اللَّوْحَةُ جَمِيلَةٌ .

Further reading practice with sun and moon letters

2. تَفْتَحُ هَذِهِ الْبِنْتُ النَّافِذَةَ .

This girl is opening the window.

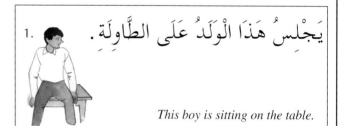

1. يَجْلِسُ هَذَا الْوَلَدُ عَلَى الطَّاوِلَةِ .

This boy is sitting on the table.

4. تَطْبَعُ هَذِهِ الْمَرْأَةُ عَلَى الْحَاسُوبِ .

This woman is typing on the computer.

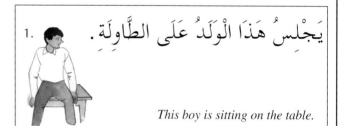

3. يَقْرَأُ هَذَا الرَّجُلُ الْجَرِيدَةَ .

This man is reading the newspaper.

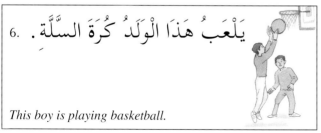

6. يَلْعَبُ هَذَا الْوَلَدُ كُرَةَ السَّلَّةِ .

This boy is playing basketball.

5. تَرْكَبُ هَذِهِ الْبِنْتُ الدَّرَّاجَةَ .

This girl is riding the bicycle.

8. تَشْرَبُ هَذِهِ الْمَرْأَةُ الْحَلِيبَ .

This woman is drinking the milk.

7. يَمْشُطُ هَذَا الْوَلَدُ الشَّعْرَ .

This boy is combing the hair.

Dialogue 1: Who is this?

Classroom Activity	Vocabulary					
Practise introducing yourself to your friends in Arabic. Ask your friend who another person in the classroom is by saying either 'Who is this?' or 'Who is that boy/girl?' in Arabic.			a girl	بِنْتٌ	I	أَنَا
	this (m.)	هَذَا	he (is)	هُوَ	that (m.)	ذَلِكَ	who?	مَنْ؟
	this (f.)	هَذِه	she (is)	هِيَ	that (f.)	تِلْكَ	a boy	وَلَدٌ

65

Dialogue 2: What's your name?

سَمير: اِسْمِي سَمير. وَمَا اسْمُكَ أَنْتَ؟

صَابِر: اِسْمِي صَابِر.

سَمير: مَرْحَبا بِكَ يَا صَابِر.

صَابِر: أَهْلاً بِكَ يَا سَمير.

سَمير: فُرْصَةٌ سَعيدَةٌ.

صَابِر: فُرْصَةٌ سَعيدَةٌ.

حَميدَة: اِسْمِي حَميدَة. وَمَا اسْمُكِ أَنْتِ؟

نَبيلَة: اِسْمِي نَبيلَة.

حَميدَة: مَرْحَبا بِكِ يَا نَبيلَة.

نَبيلَة: أَهْلاً بِكِ يَا حَميدَة.

حَميدَة: فُرْصَةٌ سَعيدَةٌ.

نَبيلَة: فُرْصَةٌ سَعيدَةٌ.

أَحْمَد: مَنْ ذَلِكَ الْوَلَدُ؟

سَمير: هُوَ صَديقِي.

أَحْمَد: مَا اسْمُهُ؟

سَمير: اِسْمُهُ صَابِر.

هُدَى: مَنْ تِلْكَ الْبِنْتُ؟

حَميدَة: هِيَ صَديقَتِي.

هُدَى: مَا اسْمُهَا؟

حَميدَة: اِسْمُهَا نَبيلَة.

friend (m.)	صَديقٌ	O! (used when addressing someone)	يَا	you (m.)	أَنْتَ	my name (is) اِسْمِي
friend (f.)	صَديقَةٌ	opportunity	فُرْصَةٌ	you (f.)	أَنْتِ	your (m.) name (is) اسْمُكَ
my friend (m.)	صَديقِي	happy	سَعيدَةٌ	hello (m.)	مَرْحَبا بِكَ	your (f.) name (is) اسْمُكِ
my friend (f.)	صَديقَتِي	When used together: 'Pleased to meet you'	فُرْصَةٌ سَعيدَةٌ	hello (f.)	مَرْحَبا بِكِ	his name (is) اسْمُهُ
				welcome (m.)	أَهْلاً بِكَ	her name (is) اِسْمُهَا
				welcome (f.)	أَهْلاً بِكِ	what? مَا؟

66

Dialogue 3: Where is your friend?

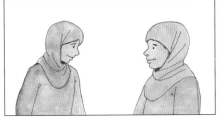

هُدَى : اَلسَّلَامُ عَلَيْكُمْ.

حَمِيدَة : وَعَلَيْكُمُ السَّلَامُ.

هُدَى : أَيْنَ صَدِيقَتُكِ الْيَوْمَ؟

حَمِيدَة : هِيَ ...

أَحْمَد : اَلسَّلَامُ عَلَيْكُمْ.

سَمِير : وَعَلَيْكُمُ السَّلَامُ.

أَحْمَد : أَيْنَ صَدِيقُكَ الْيَوْمَ؟

سَمِير : هُوَ ...

Vocabulary

اَلسَّلَامُ عَلَيْكُمْ.

Peace be upon you.

وَعَلَيْكُمُ السَّلَامُ.

(Reply): And upon you be peace.

where (is)?	أَيْنَ ؟
today	الْيَوْمَ
your friend (m.)	صَدِيقُكَ
your friend (f.)	صَدِيقَتُكِ
in	فِي

... فِي الْمَكْتَبَةِ.

in the library

... فِي الْمَلْعَبِ.

in the playground

... فِي الْمَسْجِدِ.

in the mosque

... فِي قَاعَةِ الرِّيَاضَةِ.

in the sports hall

... فِي الْمِرْحَاضِ.

in the toilet

... فِي مَكْتَبِ الْمُدِيرِ.

in the headteacher's office

... فِي قَاعَةِ الطَّعَامِ.

in the dining hall

... فِي الْفَصْلِ.

in the classroom

Dialogue 4: Goodbye

فَوْزِيَّة: مَسَاءُ الْخَيْرِ.	سَمِير: صَبَاحُ الْخَيْرِ.
لِينَا: مَسَاءُ النُّورِ.	صَابِر: صَبَاحُ النُّورِ.
فَوْزِيَّة: كَيْفَ حَالُكِ؟	سَمِير: كَيْفَ حَالُكَ؟
لِينَا: بِخَيْرٍ وَالْحَمْدُ لِلَّه.	صَابِر: بِخَيْرٍ وَالْحَمْدُ لِلَّه.
فَوْزِيَّة: وَأَنْتِ كَيْفَ صِحَّتُكِ؟	سَمِير: وَأَنْتَ كَيْفَ صِحَّتُكَ؟
لِينَا: بِخَيْرٍ وَالْحَمْدُ لِلَّه.	صَابِر: بِخَيْرٍ وَالْحَمْدُ لِلَّه.
فَوْزِيَّة: مَعَ السَّلَامَة.	سَمِير: مَعَ السَّلَامَة.
لِينَا: مَعَ السَّلَامَةِ. إِلَى اللِّقَاءِ.	صَابِر: مَعَ السَّلَامَة. فِي أَمَانِ اللَّهِ.

how are you? (m.)	كَيْفَ حَالُكَ؟	meet, meeting	لِقَاءٌ	praise	حَمْدٌ	morning	صَبَاحٌ
how are you? (f.)	كَيْفَ حَالُكِ؟	good morning	صَبَاحُ الْخَيْرِ	God, Allah	اللَّهُ	evening	مَسَاءٌ
goodbye	مَعَ السَّلَامَةِ	(reply) good morning	صَبَاحُ النُّورِ	to God	لِلَّهِ	good, well	خَيْرٌ
[Go] in God's protection	فِي أَمَانِ اللَّهِ	good evening	مَسَاءُ الْخَيْرِ	health	صِحَّةٌ	light	نُورٌ
until we meet again	إِلَى اللِّقَاءِ	(reply) good evening	مَسَاءُ النُّورِ	with	مَعَ	how?	كَيْفَ؟
		how is your (m.) health?	كَيْفَ صِحَّتُكَ؟	peace	سَلَامَةٌ	your condition, state (m.)	حَالُكَ
		how is your (f.) health?	كَيْفَ صِحَّتُكِ؟	protection	أَمَانٌ	your condition, state (f.)	حَالُكِ
		praise be to God	اَلْحَمْدُ لِلَّهِ	to, until	إِلَى	well, good	بِخَيْرٍ